Openings

DEMENTIA POEMS & PHOTOGRAPHS

John Killick & Carl Cordonnier

Published by the
Journal of Dementia Care

OPENINGS

First published in 2000 by
Hawker Publications Ltd
13 Park House
140 Battersea Park Road
London SW11 4NB
Tel 020 7720 2108, fax 020 7498 3023

British Library Cataloguing in Publication Data
A Catalogue in Publication Data
ISBN 1 874790 49 3

Designed by Andrew Chapman and Sue Lishman

Printed and bound by Hubbard Printers, Sheffield

Hawker Publications publishes *The Journal of Dementia Care.*
For further information please contact the address above.

Also published by Hawker Publications:
You Are Words – Dementia Poems, by John Killick. £6.50.
ISBN 1 874790 32 9. 1997, reprinted 2000.
Available from Hawker Publications as above or through reputable bookshops.

FOREWORD

By Faith Gibson, Professor Emeritus in Social Work, University of Ulster

In this remarkable book we catch glimpses of what it must be like to have dementia. Here are clues of how the world seems to be for people with dementia and how relationships and environments either enrich or diminish. All photography, indeed all poetry, is selective and interpretative, and this collection is no exception. These poems by John Killick and photographs by Carl Cordonnier capture particular truths about individuals, yet collectively they show common aspects of dementia: despair, desolation, fear, frustration, loss, loneliness, pain, restlessness, seeking and searching. Here too we find happiness, past and present, acute observation, perceptive comment, resistance, and sardonic humour as people struggle to express a sense of who they are and what they want; for in dementia, although much is lost, much remains.

This book could radically transform our response to dementia. It challenges our ideas about care environments, the nature of dementia, and how people resist its erosion of their fragile identities. The images, refracted through the double lens of poet and photographer, demand from the reader emotional, intellectual and behavioural reactions. We see and see again the courage, individuality, humanity and personhood of the men and women represented. The authors take the people they portray seriously and ask we do the same.

Just as the camera enlarges our world in space and time these poems enlarge our vision and extend our understanding. We catch a glimpse of the condition and state to which dementia reduces people. But to say reduces may be to misinterpret what we see and what we read, for the images, self-talk and self-reflection reveal the resilience of the human spirit under threat.

Because John Killick listens so attentively and captures so accurately the mood which accompanies the words, personhood shines through. As readers and viewers we experience a kind of double exposure whose intensity and poignancy increases our empathy, captures our imagination and compels changes in our behaviour. This book will repay careful reflection and repeated reading. It appeals at different levels. It is art, it is information, it is stimulus. It evokes more than appreciation; it demands response.

INTRODUCTION

This book was born on a day in July 1999 at the Alzheimer Europe Conference in London. I was introduced to the photographer Carl Cordonnier and saw some of his work. I immediately wanted to collaborate with him. Sue Benson of Hawker Publications was there too and was similarly enthused by Carl's photographs. They had produced a book of my Dementia Poems *You Are Words* in 1997 and were happy to consider a follow-up volume.

But this is a follow-up with a difference. I see the poems and photographs as having equal status. Each catches a person in characteristic pose and, whether through word or image, is in some way expressive of an aspect of the life of that individual. There are only two people in the poems, myself and the person with dementia, and mine is a non-speaking role. Apart from Carl and his subject there may be other people in the photographs and some interaction with them, but the focus remains on the person with the condition. Carl does not appear either, but he and I are constant presences: the angles and lighting of the pictures and the arrangement of words on the page are our contribution.

None of the pictures was taken to match the poem it accompanies, nor vice versa. In each case a marriage has been arranged, and as with all marriages some work better than others. We hope that the various juxtapositions set up meaningful resonances. In *You Are Words* I provided introductions to groups of poems, but here we are trusting that the combined art-forms will tell their own stories. The title of the book, *Openings*, was chosen to indicate the object of the exercise: an attempt to open up the words of the person with dementia to others with the condition, to those who care for them, and hopefully to a wider audience beyond.

Next, a word about how the poems came into being. I have been fortunate for the past eight years to have worked as Writer in Residence for Westminster Health Care, a private provider of nursing homes on a national scale, many of which have specialist units for people with dementia. This is, I believe, an appointment unique in the private or public sector and represents a remarkable commitment to the lives of those with the condition. It has given me the time and the opportunity to get to know a large number of people with dementia, and some of their words have been transcribed and turned into poems. I have edited their utterances but have added nothing. Everyone represented here has a diagnosis of dementia, but some have other disabilities as well. For example, the author of "Moving On" has learning difficulties too. The author of "Two Portraits" and "Nae Oniebody" (the same person as the author of the prizewinning "Nae Oniethin" in *You Are Words*) probably has schizophrenia as well as dementia. I wrote down the texts of all the poems, sometimes from tape-recordings, except one: "Nae Oniebody" was written down by its author. I should like to pay tribute to the twenty-two men and women who have contributed so much of themselves in the poems printed here.

When *You Are Words* was published the world of dementia care still seemed reluctant to accept that the person with dementia has a voice to be heard or meaningful views to express. But things have moved fast. Few people now doubt that personhood remains, and I should like to think that little book of poems made some contribution to the sea-change in attitude by providing striking and memorable instances of continued awareness and acute perspectives on all sorts of issues. Now the questions are "What exactly are people telling us?" and "How can we create the conditions which will encourage individuals to express their ideas and opinions?" I hope this new book will take its place alongside other explorations of the new territory that is opening up.

JOHN KILLICK

THE PHOTOGRAPHS

These photographs were taken as part of a project I undertook with Dr Florence Lebert of Lille, in northern France. Our purpose was to inform medical teams, nurses and other care workers of the nature of Alzheimer's disease, how it differs from very old age and the burden of care that falls on families. We chose six European countries – France, Spain, Greece, Ireland, Sweden, Germany – to give photographic, social and cultural diversity.

I began the work without any preconceptions or visual images related to dementia. I searched for signs and symbols through which to reveal both central truth and illuminating detail. Families and nurses talked to me about instants of clarity, like a window opening and closing very quickly. These flashes maintain the hope that their relative remains the same person as before.

I followed and accompanied people with dementia and their families, sitting beside them, shooting close up. I have tried to build a photographic story around each character, juxtaposing, combining and opposing images. The outcome is not an end but a beginning: a collection of faces, for memory.

CARL CORDONNIER

Openings

It's really scary when you're an old woman.
I'm bereft. I hate being stranded like this,
I want to be in the middle of town.
But I have no money to speak of,
and I don't know how to get away from here.
I can't open it! The door won't open!

I shall have to grit my teeth and walk like hell.
And it's cold out there without a coat.
How stupid I didn't think of this before.
I've never been in such a situation.
I've missed buses, but this is different.
This door won't open! And that's another!

I didn't expect this predicament. Well, if I'm stuck
I'll just have to ask them for a bed for the night.

Questions and Answers

What are we like here?
Well, we're too wideawake
to be told what to do.

What do I think of it here?
Well, it's better than
working in the wash-house!

What do people walk like that for?
Well, it's the way
they tighten us off.

How does my eye come out?
Well, it's as if it's
going to walk through that door.

Memories that Bless and Burn

Time goes by and I am still here.

I was a model in my young days – Mummy taught me.
I used to put on beautiful clothes and walk about –
north, south, east, west. I used to meet nice people,
some with lots of money. I was 18 at that time.
I sang and was an actress – just small parts.

Memories that Bless and Burn!

I was set to go to a Stage School, but they said
"You've got it, just get up and do it."
I went to a London Fashion School, but they said
"You've got it, just get up and do it."
So I left. And sometimes they would say
"You can have that dress, Folly."

I used to like bathing costumes. I had very long
jet black hair. I could sit on it. They used to call me
"Folly with the Long Sit-Upon Hair."

Oh goshee gosh gosh!

I was always working. I stayed in the hotels
where I was working. I had a car and I travelled
all over. All my photographs have gone.

They took the lot. They might have left me one,
lovely.

Memories that Bless and Burn!

I was married three times. They were all handsome,
but I cannot remember their names. Then I was alone
for a long time. My hair went all white.
I think I did too much work.

Oh goshee gosh gosh!

My house, I haven't seen it in ages. I have been here
some time. I think I get lonely because they have all gone.
And I am such an old lady.

When I think about the old days —- ah, Memories,
Memories!

I should love to have another letter from my son.
Gosh, that would be good. And some photographs of
the children.
Why don't they write? I can't remember doing anything
wrong.
When I think about the old days – oh goshee gosh!

Time goes by and I am still here.

I Mean What I Say

I'm a very intelligent person
I mean what I say
Commonsense, honesty, cleanliness – all these things

I don't smoke, I don't drink
I don't eat to excess
I still enjoy myself, even though I'm suffering

I only get energetic in bed
Only occasionally, only last Friday
I still enjoy myself, even though I'm suffering

A female came to visit me
I made her a cup of coffee
I talked to her, I didn't do anything to her

I touched her, and this and that
I kissed her, I cuddled her – all those things
But nothing more, commonsense prevailed

I look them straight in the eye
Even if it means hard labour
I have my say, even though I'm suffering

Happiness, suffering, commonsense – all these things
I mean what I say
I'm a very intelligent person

Couplets

I need to wind the clocks.
Take me to wind the clocks.

I'm frightened.
I'm frightened of being caught in a current.

It's a breast-up.
You're in need of a breast, and I'm up.

I can't get comfortable.
In my mind I can't get comfortable.

How come you stop talking
when you're talking? – you shouldn't do that.

You're a barrican. That's something you don't expect
to be good but turns out better than expected. That's you.

And now I'm going to ask you a question:
would you like to live like this?

Two Portraits

In a mansion in Monymusk
my godfather found me.
I've always been up:
he put me on his shoulder
and put my hands together –
he always had a forefinger
and a thumb around his wrist.
He says "I'll take a wander."

I was the one for him
and he gave me everything.
He looked at everything else
and the hate was real.
He kept a pet creature;
it lived on insects, slugs or weeds,
and it couldn't speak.

There was a piggery and a porcupine.
And there was a man standing.
"Are you Colonel Wilbur?" he says.
But every stall was my godfather's:
he was overall champion of the fatstock.
But they helped themselves:
they put rope halters round their necks,
and walked away with them.

Don't tell anybody –
it's a top secret –
but I'm nothing on wheels:
the motoring heart takes up everything!
Don't tell anybody –
but I have only one window:
it is made of cardboard,
and I sketched it in.

He never bothered with himself.
And I'm the same.
I never looked in a mirror,
and I never admire myself.
I've got amnesia.
And I never speak.

Glimpses

to see what is beautiful
to hear what is beautiful
they don't know what is beautiful

all these young people
good men, nice boys, fine chaps –
they are too busy to see

it'll be a good bit longer
before you see
what you want to see

but they don't want to see
what in some queer way
they are anxious to see

we see it very rarely
but the difference is
we are trying to see!

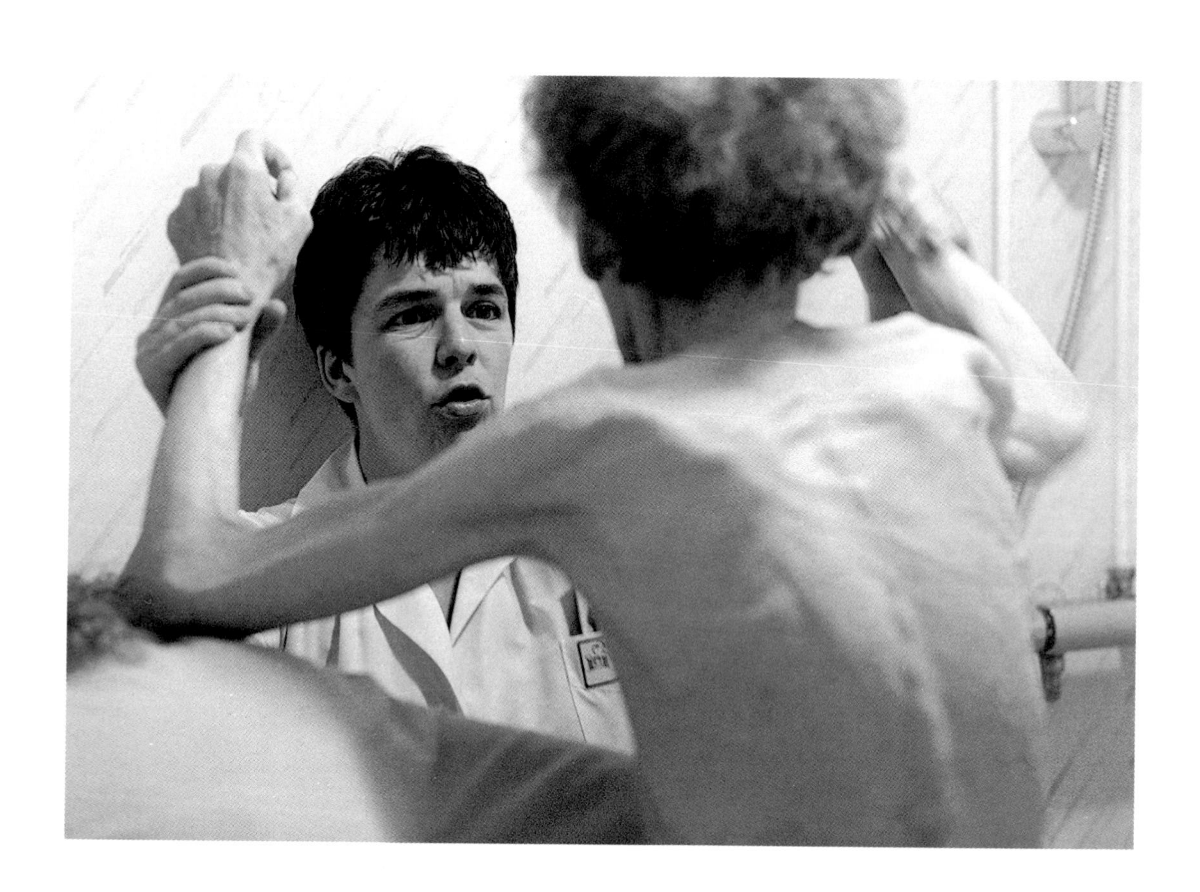

The Bad Home

God so loved the world
but He did not love this place.
All I want to do is die.
So why can't I be let to do so?
Why can't you just lay down your head?

I walk and walk and walk
but there is no God,
not in this place.
This is The Bad Home –
He has forgotten its existence.

I get up and walk till I fall.
Sinful though I be
I'll ask God for His mercy.
I'm too old to do anything.
I'm just a dustbin.

It's all the same here.
Some of the girls grasp you
as if you're a cat or a dog.
They're too young. They can't
understand the problems of age.

It's all the same here.
They're so busy,
they'll help you into anything,
even rags. You're not a person
when you come in here.

Nothing to do, nothing to say.
It's all blackness in front of me.
Another thing, they just sit there
and turn their thoughts inward.
That's why we'll never get better.

God so loved the world
but He doesn't love me.
I used to be happy,
but now I'm angry with Him
because I'm still here.

Chance

You can believe I was a doctor, if you choose to.
And I can choose to confirm it.
I still am one, and always shall be.
If they want you you have to go.

I don't plan to retire. I don't plan anything.
It's all a matter of chance, you see.
I believe in chance. I believe in
what is chosen, and that is chance too.

True Blue

I saw you when you came in.
Something about your face
puzzled me. Then I knew
it was because I knew you.
I knew your eyes. They're lovely.
The blue eyes of Paradise.

Blue eyes… blue eyes… surprise…
I can't remember it. It's from
a poem book I haven't seen
for a while. I have it
somewhere. It isn't lost.

Your eyes are blue, and your skin's
lovely. That may be flattery
but it's true. Always be true
to your own heart. I say that
because it works. I haven't always,
but I did once. And that's
something to think about.

Uninvited

Orange juice? Did you say orange juice?
Well, I haven't been asked to go.
And you haven't been asked to go.
So it's obviously not intended
that we should go on the trip.

I have told you before
that if you've got the bag
then you've got the bag.
Why did you give it to her?
I've told you before
you should have made her pay for it!

All of them in there, and those outside,
have said that those are what you're sitting in.
So there you are: where you are.
That's what you have to do.

What d'ye say? Is it hot? Well I say
it might mean so to you
but it doesn't to me!
And anyway, I haven't been asked to go.

Great Friends

Everyone who comes in here
shakes hands with me.
I always kiss the men –
I have always got on
with the gentlemen – hi, hi! –
you see, they keep on
coming in to see me!

I'm feeling sad today.
I've been going over
and over the old times.
But I have my happy days,
too, when I will smile.
Age and I are always
great friends together.

Go Away!

You have hurt me.
You have hurt me deeply!
Because you will go away.

I want to be looking
for somewhere else.
I didn't choose this place.
I don't like this area.

And oh the noise!
I can't stand the noise!
What was that sound?
It really upsets me.

I don't want to talk to you.
I don't want to see you again.
Because you will go away.

On the Move

Take yourself back to the first time
you saw them doing it. Hither and thither
and thither and thither.
It seems definitely not just
absentmindedly. It seems as if
people have something on their mind.
Going A to B to C to D to E.........
They seem to be so restless.
I think to myself they must get
awfully tired. There seems to be
an awful lot of movement.
It doesn't strike you at first.
But then everybody's doing it.
It is really rather shattering,
because you've been surprised
by others doing it, and then you find
that you are doing it yourself!

Home Alone

You know, 'tis queer – I keep getting out.
I don't know what 'tis the matter with me,
'tis the second time I've come away
and I don't know why...

I start doing work at home,
and then each time find myself in here.
I think 'tis the loneliness –
I keep going out to be with them...

I think I ought to go home,
but they're out all day.
And 'tis like coming home in here –
they always give me a bed...

When I think, which isn't very often,
I think perhaps there's nobody there,
and then my whole system churns up
and I'm in a home that stands alone...

I'll go out, and I'll get so far,
and I come to the river, and then
I'm afraid I'll not get back –
Oh in't it a queer come-along!

Moving On

I'm hoping to move on.
People come and people go.
I'm hoping to go.

I want to go somewhere else.
I've been here a long time. Too long.
I'm rather fed up.

I don't need any help.
I can drink my own tea.
I've everything I need.

If I get my new place
you can pop in now and again,
see my new room.

I can try it
and if I don't like it
I can come back.

Everybody says "You can do it."
Of course I can't do it!
But if I'm never given the chance...!

Buzz Off!

Trouble your name is!
Go and find yourself some men,
not stay with the women like this!
Go back to Yorkshire where you came from!
You know everyone's business but your own!

Lovely handwriting you've got.
It's like a woman's though.
Go, take your notebook with you!
You've got to be intelligent to do that,
but I'm sorry for you.

Hurry, Johnno, your mother's calling you.
Your sisters are after you –
there's strangers about,
and they want you home.
Stop clecking and go!

Go now, I tell you, it's getting late!
You'll be scared by the forest dark.
And you're smelling from town to town.
I haven't sent anybody from here before,
but I'm telling you now!

Nae Oniebody

'm no' a man, neither resident nor staff.
'm no' ma god-daughter, and she's no' me either.
'm no' the man called Chris on the TV Box.
'm no' oniebody bad playin' wi' a funnel.
'm no' the man that's wi' ma lassie – he's up 'n she's doon.
'm no' the resident in No 8 who won't stop singin'.
'm nae frae Alford, the village or the school, nor the
Howe o' the Mearns.
'm naebody in Arbroath, nor oniebody related to
oniebody in that toon.
'm no' time on a watch nor a ticker-Timex, nor a clock
in here.
'm no' ma aluminium walking aid, nor the colours o' the
handle,
nor the four feet o' it on ma floor.
'm no' needin' a glass o' orange for a laxative 'cos I'm
corkit.
'm no' the tail o' ma nightie that's wringin' wet, nor ma
bottom sheet.
'm no' hangers, nor who puts pants on 'em.
'm no' ma claes hangin' up there in ma room.
'm no' bags so I could give you no' one.

I'm no' oniethin' in this premises, nor even a picture
hung on the wa'
wi' a flex 'n a wee red thing.

I'm no' Woodbines in a packet, nor cheroots, nor a lime
green lighter.
I'm no' sweeties, nor Polomints, licorice straps nor Opal
Fruits.
I'm no' doughnuts, packets o' pancakes, nor girdle scones,
nor mini-mallows.
I'm no' this pale pink square oversewn at the edges wi' a
darker shade o' colour.
I'm no' ma feet, nor ma features, nor' what grows on 'em.
I'm no a bottom more nor onie man in this whoreshole.

This that I've told you is all that I can give.
But I have a name —- I'm "Jack in the Beanstalk".
It belongs to me, but I'm nae oniebody in it.

Keeping it in the Family

You didn't have a house in them days, you had rooms.
I came to live around this part, and it's a nice part, isn't it?
Now I've a house with two rooms to spare.

Are you my uncle then?

The girls were nice. Not like now when they get a bit hoity toity.
My girls quarrelled, it got a bit touchy at times.
I think it's better if you get strangers bringing them up.

You are gran's father then?

My grandmother never seemed never to make nothing hard.
My dad was a very strict man. Still is.
My man never comes in and grouses, nothing like that.

Are you one of the sons then?

All those old uns'll be gone, spent their days.
Old people today don't try to do what they shouldn't.
If there's anything here I try to keep it on the level.

Are you a bit of a relative then?

Battle of Wills

I don't mind you writing it down –
I can always alter it.

Of course I like there to be noise –
I wouldn't like to be talking to you
with nothing on the top!

Who are you? A gentleman?
No, go and look for one!

I lived on a farm. I still do.
It is higher up than this.
I'd take you there
but I wouldn't want to take you there
to start with. It is mine! It is mine!

There's nothing to say about the farm.
It's never still. Sometimes I live there,
and sometimes I don't.
Either on the farm,
or not on the farm.
I live there on my own
if there's no one there with me.

Have you seen Jackie's dog?
What kind? You'd know what kinds
it wasn't if you saw it!

Can you swim without water?
I do, every time just before I go to bed.

Between you and me, you know,
it's a battle of wills.
Why don't you just lose first!

Well you'd better go home.
Wherever that is.
For the time being.

Have You Seen my Wife?

I spend all my time wandering and looking for her.
I'll spend all afternoon up and down
the High Street and up at the Club.

If it was a man you could say "Sod off!"
Doesn't phone or nothing. You'd think
she was an armoured car.

What's that? That's not her, that's
Whatsisname, very fat, not terribly short,
but looks short against six-foot blokes!

People singing all the time.
Damn nuisance – they're always looking back,
and that's absolute murder.

I haven't eaten and I'm hungry.
I'll go round the corner, crouch down
and be a grandchild. Of course,
if you can knock something up........
I'll go through it like a scythe!

The Blue Far Yonder

In the skies up high
with the clouds below you —-
that's where I'd like to be.

With the birds,
the little sparrows,
but I'll remain a man.

It's an attraction,
it's the spaces
that we can't reach.

I was up there one day
and got the sensation
I didn't want to come down.

I'd rather be
a creature of the air
than of the earth.

From my Crying Book

There is a time for picking it up.
I sift it and the rest goes down.

I think about it all. Everything.
And everything that's left I leave.

Ever since I've been walking, talking,
I've been singing, singing so many.

There is a garden, and it's out.
She calls me back there anyway.

My mother pushed me on the swing,
singing and swinging on the wing.

She always kept an eye on us –
she couldn't keep a wink to herself.

Now she's going to be one of the betime worlds
a part of me is really sad.

I'd known nothing of the mental fare:
I wouldn't want to fade to white.

These are lines from my crying book.
I sift it and the rest goes down.

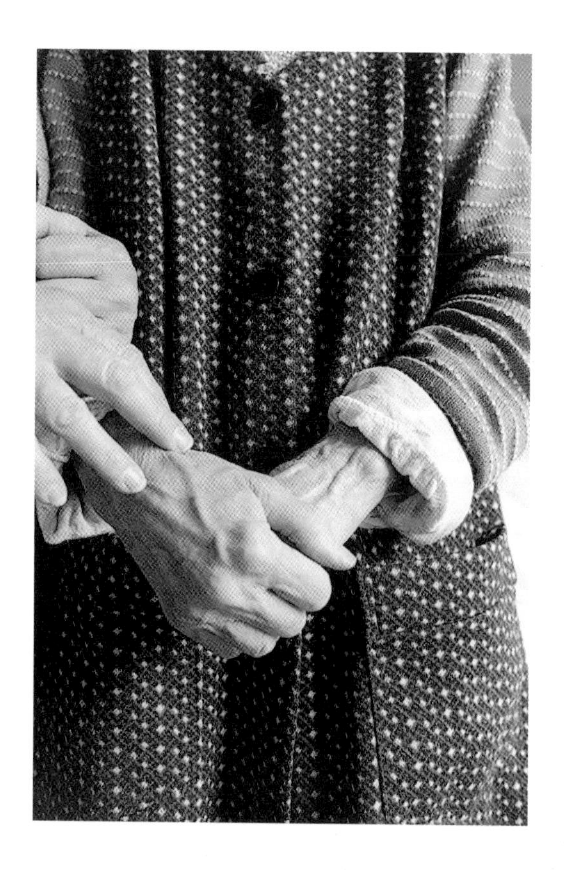